Verses From The UK

Edited By Daisy Job

First published in Great Britain in 2017 by:

Young Writers
Remus House
Coltsfoot Drive
Peterborough
PE2 9BF
Telephone: 01733 890066
Website: www.youngwriters.co.uk

Book Design by Spencer Hart

SB ISBN 978-1-78820-447-7
Printed and bound in the UK by BookPrintingUK
Website: www.bookprintinguk.com
YB0333AY

Foreword

Dear Reader,

Welcome to this book packed full of feathery, furry and scaly friends!

Young Writers' Poetry Safari competition was specifically designed for 5-7 year-olds as a fun introduction to poetry and as a way to think about the world of animals. They could write about pets, exotic animals, dinosaurs and you'll even find a few crazy creatures that have never been seen before! From this starting point, the poems could be as simple or as elaborate as the writer wanted, using imagination and descriptive language.

Given the young age of the entrants, we have tried to include as many poems as possible. Here at Young Writers we believe that seeing their work in print will inspire a love of reading and writing and give these young poets the confidence to develop their skills in the future. Poetry is a wonderful way to introduce young children to the idea of rhyme and rhythm and helps learning and development of communication, language and literacy skills.

These young poets have used their creative writing abilities, sentence structure skills, thoughtful vocabulary and most importantly, their imaginations, to make their poems and the animals within them come alive. I hope you enjoy reading them as much as we have.

Daisy Job

Contents

Inglewood Infant School, Harraby

Mayson Currie (7)	54
Sophie Moscrop (7)	55
Keanu Galbraith (7)	56
Megan Louise Dixon (6)	57
Oliver Lee Hickson (7)	58
Zac Graham (7)	59
Teigan Sophie Ayre (6)	60
Isabelle Kelso (7)	61
Jakobi Zane Hewitt (7)	62
Lexi Graham (7)	63
Natan Wojcik (6)	64
Alex Johnston (7)	65
Aidan Lowry (7)	66
Lucas William Howe (7)	67
Alisha Irwin (7)	68
Mylie Susan Small (7)	69
Kimberley Nattrass (5)	70
Olivia Louise Dowell (7)	71
Rubie Rose Forrester (7)	72
Mason Archibald (7)	73
Ayse Joan Idara (7)	74
Noah Stokoe-Douglass (6)	75
Maisey Lambert (7)	76
Jay Wharmby (7)	77
Ellis Graham (6)	78
Sophia Hammond (6)	79
Ben Galloway (6)	80
Frankie Thompson (6)	81
Paige Hayhow (7)	82
Liliya Rose Roberts (6)	83
Dylan Queen (7)	84
Logan Dunn (7)	85
Freya Harkness-Vaughan (6)	86
Marlie Cara Milne (6)	87
Ashleigh Kelly (6)	88
Jacob Matthews (5)	89
Jenson Macdonald (6)	90
Bianca Tabarda (5)	91
Sasha Johnson (6)	92
Ellis Graves (5)	93
Erin Carter (6)	94
Lynk Johnson (4)	95
Alexia Jasmine Dowell (6)	96
Will McGarvie (7)	97
Keelan Anthony Ellis (5)	98
Keegan Paul Johnston (7)	99
Daniel Mason (5)	100
Jay McCann-Lindsay (6)	101
Liam Kelly (4)	102
Caleb Pattinson (5)	103
Bayleigh Jenkinson (5)	104
Rebecca McEwan-Douglas (5)	105
Lily Elizabeth Johnston (5)	106
Harry Mellor (5)	107
Indie Rose Armstrong (4)	108
Eugene Brown (5)	109
Summer Barnes (5)	110
Mia Lamb (5)	111
Jayden-Lee Smith (5)	112
Ellie-May Dixon (5)	113
Daniel James Wharmby (4)	114

Newtownabbey Independent Christian School, Glengormley

Heidi Clarke (5)	115
Alfred Clarke (7)	116
Philip Woods (7)	117
Jedd Gegantoca (7)	118
Zac Hanna (5)	119
Sophia Hanna (7)	120

The Poems

Untitled

It's as cuddly as a teddy bear.
It's as cute as a baby.
It's as small as a mouse.
It's as soft as a blanket.
It's as sweet as a strawberry.
Can you guess what it is?

It's a kitten!

Frank Dumnoi (7)

Koala Bear

K ayla is scared of koala bear
O h a koala bear, argh run!
A koala bear is hairy and grey
L aurie loves them, but I don't
A rgh! Laurie, why are you not running, they're dangerous?

B ears are better than koala bears
E eek! It's been a long time since I have seen one
'A re you scared?' said Laurie. 'No!' said Kayla
R uby likes koala bears like me.

Ruby Hook (7)
Ballysally Primary School, Ballysally

Crocodile

C rocodiles can be many different colours
R oaring animals can fight other ones
O ver and under the crocodile goes
C rocodiles can eat big bears
O n the forest floor the crocodile walks
D own in the jungle
I saw a crocodile
L ives in the swamp
E very crocodile hunts.

Caleb Byford (7)
Ballysally Primary School, Ballysally

Gorilla

G orillas are big and strong
O ther animals are scared of gorillas
R ight, we are going to see it
I saw it was big and scary
L ots of animals are scared of gorillas
L ots of signs of gorillas, you could find one
A lost baby animal is easy to eat, one gulp.

Andzelika Krigena (7)
Ballysally Primary School, Ballysally

Tigers

T iger likes to eat meat with peppers
I better run in case I get eaten
G et back in the jungle with all the other animals
E veryone get out of the jungle, it's bad
R un away as fast as you can
S hh! There's another tiger, I want to get a picture.

Holly Holmes (7)
Ballysally Primary School, Ballysally

Giraffe

G iraffes eat from trees
I t is tall so it can see far
R eaches into tall trees
A giraffe lives on the forest floor
F orest floor is where you find it
F avourite foods are leaves and flower
shoots
E ats all day.

Stella Stewart (7)
Ballysally Primary School, Ballysally

Cheetah

C heetahs hunt a lot
H unting is good for cheetahs
E at a lot in the jungle
E ating is good for cheetahs too
T igers try to eat cheetahs
A rgh! Run away from the cheetah
H ave you ever seen one?

Laurie Milliken (7)
Ballysally Primary School, Ballysally

Iguana

I guanas camouflage in trees
G od made the iguanas
U nderstory is where iguanas live
A n iguana hunts for fruit in the jungles
N o iguana doesn't eat and camouflage
A n iguana likes the trees.

Troy Smyth (8)
Ballysally Primary School, Ballysally

Tiger

T igers eat meat
I think that tigers are very big
G irl tigers and boy tigers are very scary
E ach tiger that lives in the jungle live on
the forest floor
R *oar, roar*, tigers roar.

Olivia Lowry-Boreland (7)
Ballysally Primary School, Ballysally

Pythons

P ythons are long and short
Y ou might get eaten
T he pythons lay eggs
H op into the trees
O n pythons they have skin
N o legs on pythons
S ome pythons can bite.

Millie Wallace (8)
Ballysally Primary School, Ballysally

Macaws

M acaws are the most beautiful animals
A macaw loves to eat worms
C ome on, let's see the macaws today
A macaw is a rainbow bird
W hat are we doing? We're going to macaws.

Heidi Owens (7)
Ballysally Primary School, Ballysally

Bear

B ears are scary but not this one
E veryone comes to see the world's cutest
A w! No is that what I hear? Is that a big bear?
R ain falls down, argh! Bears break the walls, everyone run!

Lucy Hynds (7)
Ballysally Primary School, Ballysally

Panda

P eople like pandas, they are nice to people too
A nd we think they're cute too
N o way they eat meat
D on't you know they climb trees
A nd they are good climbers.

Oscar O'Neill (7)
Ballysally Primary School, Ballysally

Panda

P andas eat bamboo for tea
A person would wash pandas every day
N avigating pandas is hard
D uring dinner pandas do their business
A panda is cute even a little.

Olivia Newton (7)
Ballysally Primary School, Ballysally

Panda

P andas are soft and cute
A nd they eat bamboo in trees
N ow they are in danger
D on't ever go to the jungle
A nd they are very fluffy like my dog, Lily.

Jessica Dunn (7)
Ballysally Primary School, Ballysally

Cheetah

C heetahs are fast
H airy and soft
E ats animals
E ats fish
T old you they are funny
A ggressive sometimes
H andsome and funny.

Ollie Orr (7)
Ballysally Primary School, Ballysally

Panda

P eople think pandas are cute
A t the jungle pandas climb
N o panda can be hard
D ancing through the trees
A t the jungle they all eat bamboo.

Sade Ilori (7)
Ballysally Primary School, Ballysally

Panda

P eople think pandas are cute
A panda is chubby and cute
N ice and cuddly
D id you know pandas live in trees?
A panda eats bamboo.

Macey-Leigh McKeegan (6)
Ballysally Primary School, Ballysally

Panda

P andas are black and white
A nd pandas are fat
N ow there are lots of pandas
D id you know about them?
A panda is funny.

Bailie Montgomery (6)
Ballysally Primary School, Ballysally

Tiger

T igers roar loudly
I t can eat you
G et out of here before it eats you
E ats lots of fish and meat
R uby hates tigers.

Kayla Anne Campbell (7)
Ballysally Primary School, Ballysally

Lion

L ions eat fish and other animals
I t is very good at jumping
O h, they have sharp teeth
N o way, they have sharp claws!

Amy Moore (7)
Ballysally Primary School, Ballysally

Bears

B ears like to eat fish
E very time bears are fat
A nimals are the worst
R ough and tough to eat.

Kai Daly-Henry (7)
Ballysally Primary School, Ballysally

The Panda

Chomp, chomp, chomp!
Hungry, fluffy pandas go *crunch, crunch,*
crunch through the bamboo.

Scratch, scratch, scratch!
The panda's jaws rip into his food
like angry dinosaurs ripping their meat.

Crinkle, crackle, crinkle!
The panda's feet go crackle
through the twigs like egg shells.

Ruby Eve Fallon (5)
Berkswich CE (C) Primary School, Walton

The Penguins

Splish, splash, splish!
Furry little penguins go widdle woddle
through the herd like they're walking
with ants in their pants.
Jiggle, jiggle, jiggle!
The penguins fluffy fins wave
while they jiggle like wiggly worms
Slip, slide, slip!
The little penguins' feet slip and slide
like dancing on ice.

Eva Catherine Bhageerutty (6)
Berkswich CE (C) Primary School, Walton

The Lion

Tiptoe, tiptoe, tiptoe!
A mini lion tiptoes
through the forest
like a waterfall.

Chomp, chomp, chomp!
Eating the green leaves
high up above the sky
till he is full like a hungry fish.

Happily, happily, happily!
Funny lion enjoying the sun,
hoping to have a sunbathe
and enjoying a swim.

Lily Cooper (6)
Berkswich CE (C) Primary School, Walton

The Panda

Pant, pant, pant!
Plump pandas climb up a bamboo
slowly like a sloth.
Crunch, crunch, crunch!
Plump pandas chomp on sweet bamboo
hungrily like a tiger.
Bang, bang, bang!
Plump pandas tumble through
quickly like a rabbit.
Ffff, ffff, ffff!
Plump pandas drink water like a fish.

Elizabeth Catherine Beeson (6)
Berkswich CE (C) Primary School, Walton

The Elephant

Splash, splash, splash!
The loud elephant splashes
through the river like a submarine.

March, march, march!
The marching elephant
crashes through the forest like a soldier.

Stomp, stomp, stomp!
The angry elephant
stomping round in circles.

Hollie Jones (6)
Berkswich CE (C) Primary School, Walton

The Cobra

Shsss, shsss, shsss!
Sneaky cobras slither
through the desert like a snail.

Zoom, zoom, zoom!
Zebras zoom, like a fierce cheetah.

Roll, roll, roll!
Rats roll through the jungle like acrobats.

Charlie Dylan Dalgarno (6)
Berkswich CE (C) Primary School, Walton

The Cheetahs

Slurp, slurp, slurp, it's an elephant
Slurping like a thirsty dog.
Chomp, chomp, chomp, it's a panda
Chomp like a crocodile.
Rumble, rumble, rumble,
It's a rhino rumbling like a volcano.

Oscar Mardling (6)
Berkswich CE (C) Primary School, Walton

The Monkey

Tickle, tickle, tickle!
Playful monkeys play like a puppy.

Yum, yum, yum!
Little monkeys eat their food
Like a hungry baby.

Yawn, yawn, yawn!
Tired monkeys sleep like tortoises.

Elsie Derrick (6)
Berkswich CE (C) Primary School, Walton

The Lion

Leap, leap, leap!
A fierce lion leaps
through the jungle like an antelope
Munch, munch, munch!
Happy lions munch like an elephant.
Jump, jump, jump!
Wet lions jump like a kangaroo.

Poppy Thomson (6)
Berkswich CE (C) Primary School, Walton

The Panda

Chomp, chomp, chomp!
Plump panda eating green, small leaves.
Chomp, chomp, chomp!
It's a panda chomping grass.
Rumble, rumble, rumble!
Rhino stomping like an elephant.

Elizabeth Chambers (6)
Berkswich CE (C) Primary School, Walton

Scorpion Sense Poem

Scorpions look like a small monster
With a fierce sting.
Scorpions smell like insects blood.
Scorpions sound like snapping jaws.
Scorpions taste like crunchy bones.
Scorpions feel like a bumpy fossil!

Lucas George Shaw (7)
Berkswich CE (C) Primary School, Walton

The Lion

Roar, roar, roar!
Little lions play like puppies

Snore, snore, snore!
Lazy lions sleep like babies

Claw, claw, claw!
Large lions catch their prey.

Ryan Mangwaya (6)
Berkswich CE (C) Primary School, Walton

The Giraffe

Chop, chop, chop!
Big giraffe rips green leaves.

Ow, ow, ow!
Ants clamber on little leaves.

Swish, swish, swish!
Flicks the tail of the zebra.

Neve Skibicki (5)
Berkswich CE (C) Primary School, Walton

The Panda

Pandas are cute and fluffy
they eat crunchy, chewy bamboo.
They smell like the sweet flowers
and they don't have power.
They walk but they don't talk.
Pandas are puffy but they are not warm.
They don't like flies crawling on their knees.
They have big round bellies.
They swing in the jungle
like a monkey and they sleep quietly.

Roxanne Skyla Roberts (7)
Blackshaw Moor CE (VC) First School, Blackshaw Moor

The Giraffe

Giraffes are smart
but they don't know how to do maths.
They know how to walk
but they don't know how to talk.
Don't come near or I might bite.
Don't come near
or I might give you a fright.
A giraffe with stripy fur
does not know how to 'grr'
Giraffes are fluffy and puffy
with some big, big bellies.

Ruby Christa Heath (7)
Blackshaw Moor CE (VC) First School, Blackshaw Moor

The Dancing Frog

Inside the swamp deep down...
A frog dancing in the moonlit sky
then he stopped dancing.
Over the hill the frog heard a big bang
as loud as a lions roar.
Then the frog heard a stamp and a rustle
and it was a baby leopard.
Then the frog heard a munch
and a crunch and it was a giraffe.

Seran Foy (6)
Blackshaw Moor CE (VC) First School, Blackshaw Moor

Down In The Jungle

Down in the jungle where nobody hears,
there's a frog washing his ears.
Down in the jungle where nobody sees
there's a great green frog washing its bees.
Down in the jungle where nobody runs,
there's a frog washing its gums.

Priya Annie Norris (6)
Blackshaw Moor CE (VC) First School, Blackshaw Moor

If I Were A Frog

If I was a frog I would dance in the sun,
Jump in the water and leap and twirl.
If I go under a leaf
I would sprint and do a loop
Around the leaf.
When I go in the water,
I will swim two miles.
After that I will sprint and jump.

Frank White (7)
Blackshaw Moor CE (VC) First School, Blackshaw Moor

Panda

Pandas are fluffy and puffy
with a big round belly.
They swing in the trees
as they eat bamboo.
They smell the flowers and leaves.
They live in the breeze
and they don't like the fleas,
that dance on their knees.

Bella Clowes (7)
Blackshaw Moor CE (VC) First School, Blackshaw Moor

The Giraffe

A giraffe striped with fur.
Don't come near or I might bite.
Don't come near or I might give you a fright.
Don't come near or I might get a bit mad.
I can be very bad.

Jenson Shilcock (7)
Blackshaw Moor CE (VC) First School, Blackshaw Moor

Leopards

Leopards are scary.
Leopards are fierce.
But leopards can be mean, very mean,
They're very fierce,
They run, they bite,
They give me a fright.

Joe Cruxton (6)
Blackshaw Moor CE (VC) First School, Blackshaw Moor

The Leopard

In the wide bushes of the jungle.
It eats old flesh from a panda in a bandana.
Silently creeping whilst cunningly leaping
as angry as flickering flames.

Louis Moss (7)
Blackshaw Moor CE (VC) First School, Blackshaw Moor

The Snake

The snake was by the lake,
eating some steak.
He thought it was a big cake.
Then he had a big shake,
what a mistake!

Lydia Rose Wilkinson (6)
Blackshaw Moor CE (VC) First School, Blackshaw Moor

The Hare And The Penguin

The hare and the penguin
are happy together.
They get on well in all types of weather.
They run and they swim.
They jump and they hop.
They're always going and they can't stop!

Jonah Ó Ceallaigh (7)
Gaelscoil Éadain Mhóir, Brandywell

The Cute Cheetah

I saw a little cub, it was very cute.
The little cub was very scared and it puked.
Now it's no longer a cub,
It is now a cheetah.
I know that because I looked.

Ché Ó Dochartaigh (7)
Gaelscoil Éadain Mhóir, Brandywell

Cheetah

The cheetah was hunting for its cubs.
His name was James and he was fun.
A lion saw the cheetah running
and he sat waiting in the sun.

Jesse Mac Lochlainn (7)
Gaelscoil Éadain Mhóir, Brandywell

A Little Bat

I saw a little bat in the woods
And its name was Terry.
He was scary but he was yummy.
I love jelly so I put him in my belly.

James Ó Laoghog (7)
Gaelscoil Éadain Mhóir, Brandywell

The Dog With No Name

I saw a cute dog
She did not have a name
I gave her the name Lily
But she was a silly billy.

Grace Caomhanach (7)
Gaelscoil Éadain Mhóir, Brandywell

My Snake

My snake is very hairy
But mostly scary
It is long and scaly
But I call it Haley.

Eimhear Ní Mhurchú (7)
Gaelscoil Éadain Mhóir, Brandywell

Spider Dance

Spiders are not yummy
It crawls in your tummy
It has evil eyes
It bites, guys!

Aaron O'Neill (7)
Gaelscoil Éadain Mhóir, Brandywell

A Poem About A Fish

My fish had a baby.
It was small.
But I was tall.

Leontina Nic Eafartaigh (7)
Gaelscoil Éadain Mhóir, Brandywell

Untitled

I am a type of fish
but not a very good swimmer
I am brightly-coloured with a spiny body
I am born a tiny hatchling
a miniature of my parents
When I am fully grown
I measure ten to twenty centimetres
I hide easily in seaweed
and suck up food through my snout
What am I?

I am a seahorse.

Mayson Currie (7)
Inglewood Infant School, Harraby

A Sea Riddle

I can be orange, white, purple and yellow
When I move I move slowly
on the big hard rocks.
I hide in the green, sticky seaweed.
I eat mussels which is a bit like meat
I can be small
and I can have five or more legs
I have sucky, slimy suckers on my legs
What am I?

I'm a starfish.

Sophie Moscrop (7)
Inglewood Infant School, Harraby

Super Lob

I have ten legs.
I eat shrimp, also fish, mollusks
And other lobsters.
I shed my shell.
I have sharp tentacles.
I have a poisonous tail.
I can live up to fifty years.
I have pincers.
I can live in fresh water.
On my head I have tentacles.
I have big enormous hands.
I am a... lobster.

Keanu Galbraith (7)
Inglewood Infant School, Harraby

An Ocean Riddle

I come in loads of different
shapes and sizes
I move very quickly
through the ocean.
I eat worms, clams, mussels
snails and sea urchins
My habitat is beaches
Mostly hot countries
I behave very, very sneakily
I have two pincers and legs
What am I?

A scuttling crab!

Megan Louise Dixon (6)
Inglewood Infant School, Harraby

Ocean Riddle

I live in seas and oceans
I'd rather live in salty water
but I can survive in fresh
My body is perfectly streamlined
for fast swimming
I have a long snout and razor-sharp teeth
I am a fierce predator
I am a famous film star
What am I?

A shark.

Oliver Lee Hickson (7)
Inglewood Infant School, Harraby

Ocean Riddle

I am a type of whale
I am a little slow
I am really spotty
I live in the middle of the ocean
I am huge
I have shiny and sharp teeth
I am really brave
I weigh 19,000kg
My eyes are camouflaged into my skin
My favourite food is little fish
What am I?

Zac Graham (7)
Inglewood Infant School, Harraby

What Am I?

I have a furry tail.
I am very playful.
I sit on my owner's knee.
I am sometimes naughty
when my owner is not looking.
I have a long tail.
I am cute.
I am a purring animal.
I like running and I have whiskers.
I am spotty.
I am little.

Teigan Sophie Ayre (6)
Inglewood Infant School, Harraby

Ocean Riddle

I have a fin like a shark,
But I don't harm too many fish.
I weep to call my friends so we're safe.
We are usually found in a group.
I eat fish.
I am like a shark but I have less teeth.
I have smooth skin.
What am I?

I am a dolphin.

Isabelle Kelso (7)
Inglewood Infant School, Harraby

Ocean Riddle

In Latin people say my name like this...
Pterophyllum.
Fish like the look of me
I behave really good
I eat fish flakes or pellets
I like warm water
I have many different colours
And rainbow patterns.
I don't live in Heaven
What am I?

Jakobi Zane Hewitt (7)
Inglewood Infant School, Harraby

Ocean Riddle

I have two ears and bumpy skin.
I move by gliding along the sea and water.
I hide in the green seaweed.
I suck food through my snout.
I eat small animals like shrimp.
My snout is very long and big.
I hang onto the seaweed with my tail.
What am I?

Lexi Graham (7)
Inglewood Infant School, Harraby

What Am I?

I have long ears and a curly tail.
My body is soft
and I like eating carrots.
I can jump really high
so when it's Easter
I bring chocolate eggs for people.
I have a little nose.
I like to jump.

I am a rabbit.

Natan Wojcik (6)
Inglewood Infant School, Harraby

Rock Pool Riddle

I am orange and yellowish and red.
I have two eyes, six legs.
One shell side and two claws.
I move side to side.
I live in a rocky rock pool.
I snap at people all day long.
I eat green algae.
I like the rock pool.
What am I?

Alex Johnston (7)
Inglewood Infant School, Harraby

Ugliest Animal On The Planet

I live in the deep Antarctic
I am angry looking
I look scary
I am the ugliest animal on the planet
I feed on flesh
I can swallow prey twice my size
I try to eat my own lamp
I have a lamp on my antenna
I am an... anglerfish.

Aidan Lowry (7)
Inglewood Infant School, Harraby

Sea Creature Riddle

I can camouflage when afraid.
I am a mollusk.
I can squeeze into tight spaces.
I have three beating hearts.
I have the same legs as a spider.
I squirt a black cloud when threatened.
What am I?

I am an octopus.

Lucas William Howe (7)
Inglewood Infant School, Harraby

Ocean Riddle

I live a solitary life
I am cold-blooded
I eat stinging jellyfish, shrimps,
Green seaweed and snappy crabs
I swim very slowly
My short legs number four
My shells number two
What am I?

I am a sea turtle.

Alisha Irwin (7)
Inglewood Infant School, Harraby

Ocean Riddle

I live in lots of different types of water
but not cold water.
I move really fast in the water
I'm a mammal
so I drink milk from my mother
I like doing somersaults in the air.
What am I?

I am a dolphin.

Mylie Susan Small (7)
Inglewood Infant School, Harraby

What Am I?

I have nice soft fur
and my owners feed me fish all the time.
And I don't like dogs,
I run away from dogs.
People like me so much
and they stroke me all the time.
My owners are nice to me.

I am a cat.

Kimberley Nattrass (5)
Inglewood Infant School, Harraby

Beautiful Shine

I am a mammal.
I can only go underwater
for fifteen minutes.
I can swim up to two hundred
and sixty metres.
I live in schools or pods.
I have lots of friends.
I have a blowhole.
I am a... dolphin.

Olivia Louise Dowell (7)
Inglewood Infant School, Harraby

Shiny Stripes

I can live for a very long time.
I eat bloodworms and blackworms.
I am blue and yellow.
I have huge eyes.
There are two different kinds of me.
I can live in fresh water or rivers.
I am an... angelfish.

Rubie Rose Forrester (7)
Inglewood Infant School, Harraby

Ocean Riddle

I am big
but I can squeeze through small cracks.
I have eight long limbs.
I eat big snapping crabs.
I am really shy.
I am soft and big.
I live in rocks.
I have three hearts.
What am I?

Mason Archibald (7)
Inglewood Infant School, Harraby

Rock Pool Riddle

My favourite food is seaweed
I live in a rock pool
And have spikes and a sharp shell
I catch stones on my spikes
I move using suckers like a starfish
What am I?

I am a sea urchin.

Ayse Joan Idara (7)
Inglewood Infant School, Harraby

What Am I?

I have sharp claws.
I have terrifying teeth.
I have white and black stripes.
I like to hunt my prey.
I like to flash my teeth
and my claws.
I like to run.
I am a honey badger.

Noah Stokoe-Douglass (6)
Inglewood Infant School, Harraby

Super Smooth

I am a mammal
I can swim 260 metres
I can stay underwater for fifteen minutes
I have two fins
I can live in rivers or oceans
I make clicking and whistling noises
I am a... dolphin.

Maisey Lambert (7)
Inglewood Infant School, Harraby

Yum Yum

I can breathe underwater
I can be as big as a house
Or as small as a dwarf
I never run out of teeth
I am a fish
My fins move side to side
I have 20,000 teeth
I am a... shark.

Jay Wharmby (7)
Inglewood Infant School, Harraby

What Am I?

I have soft fur.
I like bathing.
I have horns.
I am a wild animal.
I am cute.
I am white.
I have a little pink nose.
I am medium size.
I like bumping into stuff.

Ellis Graham (6)
Inglewood Infant School, Harraby

What Am I?

I have four legs and a long tail.
I am fierce
and I like to creep in the jungle.
I have sharp teeth.
I have sharp claws.
I have got floppy ears.
I am stripy.

Sophia Hammond (6)
Inglewood Infant School, Harraby

What Am I?

I have long, sharp teeth
I live underwater
I have a long tail with two points
I like to eat fish and squid
Some people get my teeth
To wear them on their neck.

Ben Galloway (6)
Inglewood Infant School, Harraby

What Am I?

I have a spotty back and a wet tail.
I am very soft.
I love sitting on my owner's knee.
I am very playful.
I like eating food a lot.
I lick my water a lot.

Frankie Thompson (6)
Inglewood Infant School, Harraby

Super Shiny

I have a pointy, sharp fin
I am blue
I have an arrow tail
I am shiny
I eat herring, shrimp and mackerel
I curve and leap out of water
I am a... dolphin.

Paige Hayhow (7)
Inglewood Infant School, Harraby

What Am I?

I have little ears
I like swimming
I have two big teeth
I have a little tail
I am grey
I eat fish
I like rolling around in the mud
I am enormous.

Liliya Rose Roberts (6)
Inglewood Infant School, Harraby

Squirty

I live in all the oceans
I have lots of arms
My skin can change colour
I can shoot an inky fluid
I have eight legs
I am an... octopus.

Dylan Queen (7)
Inglewood Infant School, Harraby

Special Fish Riddle

I am a type of fish
I am common in the United States
I am completely shiny
I eat algae
I am nice and brave
I am gold
What am I?

Logan Dunn (7)
Inglewood Infant School, Harraby

Snake

I am a snake
I can slither
I can wiggle
I feel scaly
I smell danger
I am flexible
I am squishy
I am a snake.

Freya Harkness-Vaughan (6)
Inglewood Infant School, Harraby

Parrot

I am a parrot
I can squawk
I can fly
I feel soft
I smell through my nose
I am colourful
I am tired
I am a parrot.

Marlie Cara Milne (6)
Inglewood Infant School, Harraby

Butterfly

I am a butterfly
I can flutter
I can rest
I feel soft
I smell flowers
I am happy
I am colourful
I am a butterfly.

Ashleigh Kelly (6)
Inglewood Infant School, Harraby

Tiger

I am a tiger
I can roar
I can run
I feel soft
I smell animals
I am stripy
I am fierce

I am a tiger.

Jacob Matthews (5)
Inglewood Infant School, Harraby

Cheetah

I am a cheetah
I can run fast
I can sniff food
I feel fierce
I smell meat
I am bad
I am happy
I am a cheetah.

Jenson Macdonald (6)
Inglewood Infant School, Harraby

Lion

I am a lion
I can hunt
I can run
I feel hungry
I smell food
I am orange
I am strong

I am a lion.

Bianca Tabarda (5)
Inglewood Infant School, Harraby

What Am I?

I have a pink tongue
I have greenish eyes
and I have a scaly back.
I like to slither on my tummy.

I am a snake.

Sasha Johnson (6)
Inglewood Infant School, Harraby

Fish

I am a fish
I can swim
I can blow bubbles
I feel hard
I smell nice
I am orange

I am a fish.

Ellis Graves (5)
Inglewood Infant School, Harraby

What Am I?

I have a long, long tail.
I have fur.
I have claws.
I am a pet
and I like to purr.

I am a cat.

Erin Carter (6)
Inglewood Infant School, Harraby

The Giraffe

The giraffe has octagon shapes
The giraffe eats carrots
The giraffe is brown and yellow
The giraffe has a long neck.

Lynk Johnson (4)
Inglewood Infant School, Harraby

What Am I?

I have a furry body
I eat meat and bones
I drink water
I have whiskers
I play with my toys and with my owner.

Alexia Jasmine Dowell (6)
Inglewood Infant School, Harraby

Untitled

I weigh 200 tonnes.
I can hold my breath for so long.
People used to hunt me for my oil.
I am a... blue whale.

Will McGarvie (7)
Inglewood Infant School, Harraby

Roo

I am brown.
I have babies.
I live in a pouch.
I drink water.
I jump.
I sleep.
I have a pouch.

Keelan Anthony Ellis (5)
Inglewood Infant School, Harraby

Super Swimmer

I am so skinny and flat
I am light grey
I love eating mussels
I live in the sea
I am a... stingray.

Keegan Paul Johnston (7)
Inglewood Infant School, Harraby

What Am I?

I have soft brown fur.
I like to play in the garden
with my white tail.

I am a dog.

Daniel Mason (5)
Inglewood Infant School, Harraby

Lightning The Hamster

I have a soft body.
I drink water.
I run about in a wheel.

I am a hamster.

Jay McCann-Lindsay (6)
Inglewood Infant School, Harraby

Hoops

Hoops eats my jumper!
Hoops poos in the garden!
Hoops eats dog food!
I love Hoops!

Liam Kelly (4)
Inglewood Infant School, Harraby

Sheep Dog

The sheep dog is cute
It is fluffy
It helps the farm
Woof, woof.

Caleb Pattinson (5)
Inglewood Infant School, Harraby

Horses

Horses jump
Horses run fast
Horses 'neigh'
Horses eat hay!

Bayleigh Jenkinson (5)
Inglewood Infant School, Harraby

Ziggy The Dog

The dog is brown
He is happy
He plays with the ball
Woof!

Rebecca McEwan-Douglas (5)
Inglewood Infant School, Harraby

Rosy The Pig

The pig is fat
He is round and pink.
My pig has a nice tail
Shiny.

Lily Elizabeth Johnston (5)
Inglewood Infant School, Harraby

The Sea Snake

The sea snake is slimy
The sea snake can fight
The sea snake can bite.

Harry Mellor (5)
Inglewood Infant School, Harraby

Dilly The Dog

The dog is black and white
She is fluffy
Woof, woof, woof!

Indie Rose Armstrong (4)
Inglewood Infant School, Harraby

What Am I?

I am short
I am black with white stripes

I am a zebra.

Eugene Brown (5)
Inglewood Infant School, Harraby

Briella The Horse

The horse is nosey and noisy
The horse is eating
He eats hay.

Summer Barnes (5)
Inglewood Infant School, Harraby

Lola The Bunny

My bunny is fluffy
I love hugging my bunny
My bunny loves me.

Mia Lamb (5)
Inglewood Infant School, Harraby

Tiger

Tiger hairy
Tiger hungry
Tiger stripy
Tiger scary.

Jayden-Lee Smith (5)
Inglewood Infant School, Harraby

Oink, Oink!

Pigs roll in mud
Pigs are pink
Curly tail.

Ellie-May Dixon (5)
Inglewood Infant School, Harraby

Rhino

Rhino eats grass
Mad
Sad
Horn.

Daniel James Wharmby (4)
Inglewood Infant School, Harraby

My Dog

Willow is hairy
Willow is big
And she's a standard schnauzer.
She's black and white
She runs up and down
She jumps on sofas and people
She eats a lot
She sleeps on my bed
Sometimes she's very bad
But I think she's very cute.

Heidi Clarke (5)
Newtownabbey Independent Christian School, Glengormley

A Snail

There was a snail and the snail ate plums.
It was a nice snail and a friendly snail.
The snail is dark and light brown.
The snail is slippery and slimy
and its shell is hard.
It is as slippery as water.
It lives in my vegetable patch.

Alfred Clarke (7)
Newtownabbey Independent Christian School, Glengormley

The Slimy Snake

A slimy snake,
Slippery of water,
Slithered into its lair,
Hissing like a cat,
It wiggles like a river,
Slowly and lazily,
It makes its way,
To kill its prey,
Red for danger!

Philip Woods (7)
Newtownabbey Independent Christian School, Glengormley

The Cheetah

The cheetah loves to run
And it runs to its prey.
I wish I could run
Like a cheetah every day.

Jedd Gegantoca (7)
Newtownabbey Independent Christian School, Glengormley

My Dinosaur

My dinosaur's angry,
My dinosaur thumps,
My dinosaur jumps over trees.

Zac Hanna (5)
Newtownabbey Independent Christian School, Glengormley

About Whiskers

My cat is fluffy
It can purr,
Soft as a peach,
Fluffy as a cushion.

Sophia Hanna (7)
Newtownabbey Independent Christian School, Glengormley

Young Writers Information

We hope you have enjoyed reading this book – and that you will continue to in the coming years.

If you're a young writer who enjoys reading and creative writing, or the parent of an enthusiastic poet or story writer, do visit our website www.youngwriters.co.uk. Here you will find free competitions, workshops and games, as well as recommended reads, a poetry glossary and our blog.

If you would like to order further copies of this book, or any of our other titles give us a call or visit **www.youngwriters.co.uk**.

Young Writers, Remus House, Coltsfoot Drive, Peterborough, PE2 9BF
(01733) 890066

info@youngwriters.co.uk